WOLFGANG AMADEUS MOZART

PIANO CONCE   20

D minor/d-Moll/Re
K466

Edited by/Herausgegeben von
Paul Badura-Skoda

Ernst Eulenburg Ltd

London · Mainz · Madrid · New York · Paris · Prague · Tokyo · Toronto · Zürich

CONTENTS

Ernst Eulenburg Ltd
48 Great Marlborough Street
London W1F 7BB

PREFACE

The first performance of this, the most dramatic of all the Mozart concertos, on 11 February 1785 at the *Mehlgrube* in Vienna, must have been an exciting occasion. Mozart's father Leopold, who had arrived in Vienna only a few hours earlier, 'travelling in snow and ice, and on an absolutely ghastly road', sent the following report to Salzburg in a letter written to Mozart's sister Nannerl:

That same Friday evening we went at 6 o'clock to his first subscription concert where there was a great gathering of select people. [...] The concert was incomparable, the orchestra excellent; apart from the symphonies a [lady] singer from the Italian theatre sang two arias. Then came a new excellent piano concerto by Wolfgang which the copyist was still copying when we arrived, and your brother did not even have the time to play through the *Rondeau* as he had to supervise the copying. You can easily imagine that I met many acquaintances there and that they all came up to me.[1]

Playing the last movement of this concerto at sight might prove difficult even for the best orchestras of today. The fact that the performance failed to break down is evidence of the high degree of proficiency among orchestral musicians of the period, as well as of the efficiency of Mozart – who probably gave some vigorous support to the tutti passages – in directing the work from the piano. We can assume that Haydn was one of the acquaintances present at the first performance. Spending the following evening as guest of the Mozarts, he said to Leopold:

I tell you before God as an honest man, your son is the greatest among the composers known to me by name and person: he has good taste, and furthermore the greatest knowledge of composition.

Presumably these words of praise did not just refer to the three 'new string quartets' played on that same occasion, but also to the concerto heard the previous day.

During that period Mozart had no peace, not even after this first performance. Only two days later he played another piano concerto, probably the one in B flat, K456, in the *Akademie* (subscription concert) of the singer Luisa Laschi, who later sang the part of the Countess in the first performance of *Figaro*. Two days after that he repeated the performance of the 'great new' Concerto in D minor in the *Akademie* of the singer Elisabeth Distler at the *Burgtheater* – 'magnifique' according to Leopold Mozart,[2] referring apparently to the composition as well as to the performance.

In spite of the hectic nature of these events, the autograph of the full score (in the *Gesellschaft der Musikfreunde*, Vienna) shows no signs of haste. However, the fact that Mozart was overworked during these early months of 1785 may account for his omitting to write down his cadenzas as he did in the case of most of the other concertos – a loss for which not even the cadenzas Beethoven wrote for this concerto are consolation. The latter belong to another world, and only the first of them can be regarded as being stylistically of value.[3]

The absence of any indication of the instrumentation before the brackets at the beginning of the second movement is due to an oversight of Mozart. This has caused most later editions to indicate horns in B flat *basso* here. But we can assume that Mozart almost certainly had horns in B fat *alto* in mind. The reasons for this assumption are:

1. In Mozart's time horns in B flat *alto* were the rule, in B flat *basso* the exception.
2. In all the other concerto movements in B flat Mozart indicates horns in B flat *alto*.

---

[1] Letter from Leopold Mozart to his daughter in Salzburg, 16 February 1785

[2] ibid.
[3] See Eva and Paul Badura-Skoda, *Mozart Interpretation* (Vienna-Leipzig, 1957), 246, 253

3. If the *Romanze* were to be played with horns in B flat *basso* the resulting harmonies in b39 and bb148–9 would be false, since the second horn would have to play lower notes than the double bass and second bassoon. In the other passages, bb78–83 and bb135–6, B flat *alto* horns sound more 'like Mozart', while in bbll8–9 and b144 flat *basso* horns might sound almost better.

In determining an appropriate tempo for the second movement, two letters should be borne in mind: Mozart's of 9 June 1784 in which he warned against dragging in the central movements of his concertos, and a less well known one of Leopold Mozart's to his daughter in which he writes:

I am sending you herewith a concerto. The *Adagio*[4] is a Romance, the tempo is to be taken at the speed in which the noisy passage with the fast triplets just at the beginning of the third page of the Romance can be executed, and these must be properly practised so that the theme is not too lifeless. In the same way the tempo of the first *Allegro* must be taken according to the fast passages.[5]

An important passage in the first movement deserves a mention. In the preface to the score published earlier by Eulenburg, Friedrich Blume pointed out that the low bass notes in bb88–99 of the first movement are not playable on one piano alone without a very disturbing break in the phrasing. These low bass notes which appear in the autograph, but curiously in none of the editions, can simply be explained by the fact that Mozart disposed of a pedal piano at the concerts he played early in 1785. This instrument had been specially made for him and was mentioned in Leopold Mozart's letter of 12 March 1785:

Since my arrival your brother's fortepiano [grand] has been carried from the house to the theatre or to another house at least 12 times. He has had a big pedal-fortepiano made which stands under the grand piano, is three spans longer and surprisingly heavy; every Friday it is carried to the *Mehlgrube*, and it has also been taken to Count Cziczi and Prince Kaunitz.

A handbill announcing the *Akademie* at the *Burgtheater* on 10 March 1785 has also been preserved:

Anouncement. On Thursday, 10 March 1785 Kapellmeister Mozart will have the honour of giving a great musical Akademie for his own benefit in the Imperial-Royal National Court Theater, at which he will not only play a newly finished concerto for the fortepiano but also use a specially big pedal fortepiano for his improvisations.[6]

Conceivably Mozart wrote these low bass notes with his pedal-fortepiano in mind. It is true that this supposition is disputed in the preface to this concerto in the *New Mozart Edition*,[7] where the low bass notes are described as an interim version which had not been deleted, and where it is thought unlikely that Mozart would have entered in the score of a piano concerto pedal notes solely for one occasion. Maybe the editors of the *NME* had only a somewhat blurred photocopy at their disposal. At close examination of Mozart's autograph score it can be seen, however, that the low bass notes were written simultaneously with the chords as the final version (presumably to support the indefinite bass notes of the timpani), while an earlier one was erased by Mozart himself. The absence of the notation of such pedal notes in Mozart's other piano concertos is understandable since he could not count on other pianists having access to this specially constructed instrument. There is, however, another composition for organ or pedal piano by Mozart which evidently made allowances for such a possibility: the unfinished Fugue in G minor K401 (375e). An arrangement for piano duet used for present-day performances of this Fugue and similarly in the D minor Concerto the low bass notes could be played by another pianist sitting next to the soloist.

---

[4] Leopold Mozart uses the word 'Adagio' here of course in the sense of 'slow movement' (a term as yet not coined in those days) and not at all to imply a dragging tempo as is obvious from the meaning of the sentence

[5] Letter from Leopold Mozart to his daughter in St Gilgen, 4 January 1786

[6] *Mozart, Die Dokumente seines Lebens*, edited by Otto Erich Deutsch (Bärenreiter, Kassel, 1961), 211–2

[7] see *New Mozart Edition*, Piano Concertos, Vol.6, edited by Horst Heussner, Hans Engel (Bärenreiter, Kassel, 1961)

Furthermore, a report by the physician Frank[8] states that Mozart played in other, not specifically indicated, passages low bass notes obtainable on his pedal piano which went beyond the range of his fortepiano. On the modern grand piano such low bass notes could easily be added in the D minor Concerto, first movement b230, and in b113 in the second movement; but it is likely that Mozart used the pedal piano also on other occasions, for instance in the third movement bb148ff, and in corresponding passages.

We are further indebted to Friedrich Blume for being the first to point out in his prefaces to the Eulenburg scores that the general use of the piano as a continuo instrument, in the passages where it did not appear as soloist, was by no means merely a convention. The already quoted letter by Leopold Mozart of 4 January 1786 says: 'When I send off the other Concerto [K467] you can return this one [K466] so that I can write the figures on it.' It is hardly likely that Leopold Mozart would have taken the trouble to figure the bass of the piano part in the tutti – only wind passages had no figures – if he had not been present at performances where his son adopted this style of playing.

All the same, the constant playing of a continuo part on a modern concert grand piano – its muffled sound does not blend well with the strings – is not advisable, least of all in the *piano* passages. In the case of a certain number of *forte* passages, however, a participation in the progression of chords can still be regarded today as being beneficial to the performance, for instance in the first movement, bb112–4, in the third movement bb371ff, bb383ff, b414 and b418, but above all in the final bars. In the tutti conclusion of the B flat Piano Concerto K456 Mozart himself expressly added three continuo chords to the piano part.[9]

It can be assumed that in the second movement the subtle variations of the theme at the returns of the tutti in b81 and b141 were likewise preceded in Mozart's performance by embellished versions of the solo part eight bars earlier. The aforementioned haste in writing down the score might explain why Mozart did not bother to put down such 'mini variations' in the solo part as he did in so many other slow movements. The question whether or not one ought to attempt to play embellished versions in modern performances is a delicate one. If variations of the theme are played at all, they ought to be as subtle and tasteful as Mozart's own in other works.

Paul Badura-Skoda

[8] *Mozart, Die Dokumente seines Lebens*, loc. cit., 476

[9] see Paul Badura-Skoda, „Über das Generalbass-Spiel in Mozarts Klavierkonzerten", *Mozart Yearbook*, 1957

Editorial Notes

Only source autograph (AUT)

I

146–7	Pft	in AUT slur starts last note 146, probably Mozart's writing error (cf. VI, I, II)
165	Pft	dynamic mark missing in AUT, probably *cresc.* or *forte* intended (cf. 341)
298	Vl, II	so in AUT after correction to complete harmony
325	Vc/Cb	first two notes (only) staccato

II

8	Pft	AUT last three notes legato, missing at later entries
35	Fl/ObI	appoggiatura a quaver; in Vl I a semiquaver
98	Pft	so in AUT; other editions wrongly have F instead of E♭, at 7th and 8th quavers

III

AUT has no tempo indication. *Allegro assai* taken from earliest editions

198	Pft	AUT last note quaver instead of semiquaver, probably by error (cf. bb65 & 232)
242	Fl	AUT last note quaver; difference to 232 might be intended here due to different response of Fl to Pft

VORWORT

Bei der Uraufführung dieses wohl dramatischsten aller Mozart-Konzerte am 11. Februar 1785 auf der Mehlgrube in Wien muss es aufregend zugegangen sein. Mozarts Vater Leopold, der wenige Stunden zuvor bei „Schnee und Eyss und durchaus abscheulichem Weg" in Wien eingetroffen war, berichtet darüber in einem Brief an Mozarts Schwester Nannerl in Salzburg:

Den nämlichen Freytag abends fuhren wir um 6 uhr in sein erstes subscriptions Concert, wo eine große versamlung von Menschen von Rang war. […] Das Concert war unvergleichlich, das Orchester vortrefflich, außer den Synfonien sang eine Sängerin vom welschen Theater 2 Arien. dann war ein neues vortreffliches Clavier Concert vom Wolfgang, wo der Copist, da wir ankamen noch daran abschrieb, und dein Bruder das Rondeau noch nicht einmahl durchzuspielen Zeit hatte, weil er die Copiatur übersehen mußte. Daß (ich) nun da viele bekannte angetroffen, und mir alles zulief, kannst dir leicht vorstellen.[1]

Selbst ein modernes Spitzenorchester könnte nur unter Schwierigkeiten den Finalsatz dieses Konzertes vom Blatt spielen. Es spricht für das hohe Niveau der damaligen Orchestermusiker und für Mozarts Dirigierleistung vom Flügel aus – sicher unter kräftigem Mitspielen während der Tutti –, dass das Klavierkonzert offensichtlich erfolgreich „über die Runden ging". – Es ist wohl anzunehmen, dass auch Joseph Haydn unter den Bekannten war, die dieser Uraufführung beiwohnten. Wenn er am nächsten Abend als Gast bei Mozarts zu Vater Leopold sagte:

Ich sage ihnen vor gott, als ein ehrlicher Mann, ihr Sohn ist der größte Componist, den ich von Person und dem Namen nach kenne: er hat geschmack, und über das die größte Compositionswissenschaft,[1]

so wird dieses Lob sich nicht nur auf die frei gespielten „neuen Streichquartette", sondern wohl auch auf das am Vortag gehörte Konzert bezogen haben.

Auch nach der Uraufführung kam Mozart nicht zur Ruhe. Schon zwei Tage danach spielte er in der Akademie der Sängerin Luisa Laschi, der späteren Gräfin bei der Uraufführung des *Figaro*, ein anderes Klavierkonzert, wahrscheinlich das B-Dur-Konzert KV 456; und wieder zwei Tage danach, am 15. Februar, spielte er nochmals das „große neue" d-moll-Konzert in der Akademie der Sängerin Elisabeth Distler im Burgtheater, „magnifique" (Leopold Mozart),[2] was sich sowohl auf die Komposition wie auf die Aufführung zu beziehen scheint.

Trotz dieser turbulenten Ereignisse zeigt das Partiturautograph (Gesellschaft der Musikfreunde, Wien) keinerlei Spuren der Hast. Auf Mozarts Überbeschäftigung in diesen ersten Monaten des Jahres 1785 dürfte aber der Umstand zurückzuführen sein, dass er nicht wie bei den meisten übrigen Klavierkonzerten seine Kadenzen niederschrieb – ein Verlust, über den uns auch die stilistisch einer anderen Welt angehörenden Kadenzen Beethovens zu diesem Konzert nicht hinwegtrösten können, von denen nur die erste als gelungen bezeichnet werden kann.[3]

Am Beginn des 2. Satzes hat Mozart versehentlich vor der Akkolade keine Angaben über die Instrumentation gemacht. So konnte es geschehen, dass die meisten bisherigen Ausgaben hier Hörner in tief-B angaben. Aus folgenden Gründen ist jedoch fast mit Sicherheit anzunehmen, dass Mozart Hörner in hoch-B gemeint hat:

1. Hörner in hoch-B waren zu Mozarts Zeiten die Regel, in tief-B die Ausnahme.

---

[2] Ebda.

[3] Vgl. Eva und Paul Badura-Skoda, *Mozart Interpretation*, Wien-Leipzig 1957, S. 246 und 253. Unter den Kadenzen jüngerer Zeit, die sich um Stilnähe bemühen, seien jene von A. Brendel (Doblinger, Wien 1962), M. Flothius (Broekman & Poppels, Amsterdam 1960) und des Herausgebers (Bärenreiter, Kassel 1967) erwähnt.

[1] Brief Leopold Mozarts an seine Tochter in Salzburg, 16. Februar 1785.

2. In allen übrigen Klavierkonzertsätzen, die in B-Dur stehen, schreibt Mozart Hörner in hoch-B vor.

3. Wenn man die Romanze mit Hörnern in tief-B spielte, dann würde sich in T. 39 und T. 148–149 eine falsche Harmonie ergeben, bei der das zweite Horn tiefere Noten als der Kontrabass bzw. das zweite Fagott zu spielen hätte. Auch an zwei anderen Stellen klingen hoch-B Hörner, mozartischer' nämlich in T. 78–83 und T. 135–136, während wiederum in T. 118–119 und T. 144 tief-B Hörner fast besser wirken würden.

Zur Ermittlung des von Mozart beabsichtigen Tempos im 2. Satz geben zwei Briefe aus dieser Zeit wertvolle Hinweise: Mozarts Brief vom 9. Juni 1784, in dem er davor warnt, die Mittelsätze seiner Konzerte schleppend zu spielen, und ein wenig bekannter Brief Leopold Mozarts an Mozarts Schwester, in dem er schreibt:

Hier schicke [ich] 1 Concert. das adagio[4] ist eine Romance, das Tempo wird in der geschwindigkeit genommen, so geschwind man den Lermen mit den geschwinden Treyerl herausbringen kann, die gleich auf der 3ten Seite des Romance vorkommen, und recht müssen exerciert werden, damit das Thema nicht zu matt kommt. Eben so muß man das erste Allegro nach den geschwinden Passagen im Tempo nehmen.[5]

Eine wichtige Stelle im 1. Satz verdient noch Erwähnung: In der früheren Eulenburg-Ausgabe wies Friedrich Blume im Vorwort darauf hin, dass die tiefen Bassnoten im 1. Satz T. 88–99 ohne sehr störende Brechung von einem Klavier allein nicht zu spielen sind. Diese im Autograph stehenden in den meisten Ausgaben fehlenden, tiefen Bassnoten lassen sich dadurch zwanglos erklären, dass Mozart für die Konzerte Anfang 1785 ein Pedalklavier zur Verfügung hatte, das er sich eigens hatte anfertigen lassen. Dieses Pedalklavier wird in Leopold Mozarts Brief vom 12. März 1785 erwähnt:

Deines Bruders Fortepiano Flügel ist wenigst 12 mahl, seit dem (ich) hier bin, aus dem Hause ins Theater oder in ein anderes Haus getragen worden. er hat ein grosses Fortepiano pedale machen lassen, das unterm flügel steht und um 3 spann länger und erstaunlich schwer ist, alle freytage zur mehlgrube getragen wird, und auch zum Gr. Cziczi und Fürst Kaunitz getragen wurde.

Von der Burgtheater-Akademie am 10. März 1785 ist auch ein Handzettel erhalten:

Nachricht. Donnerstag den 10ten März 1785. wird Herr Kapellmeister Mozart die Ehre haben in dem k.k. National-Hof-Theater eine grosse musikalische Akademie zu seinem Vortheile zu geben, wobey er nicht nur ein neues erst verfertigtes Forte-piano-Konzert spielen, sondern auch ein besonders grosses Fortepiano Pedal beym Phantasieren gebrauchen wird.[6]

Offensichtlich schrieb Mozart die tiefen Bassnoten im Hinblick auf sein Pedalklavier. Diese Annahme wird allerdings in der *Neuen-Mozart-Ausgabe* bestritten[7], wo diese Noten als eine versehentlich nicht gestrichene Zwischenversion gedeutet werden und wo daran gezweifelt wird, dass Mozart nur dieses einzige Mal solche Pedalnoten niedergeschrieben hätte. Vielleicht hatten die Herausgeber der NMA nur eine etwas unscharfe Fotokopie zu ihrer Verfügung. Bei genauer Prüfung sind im Autograph nämlich nur zwei Fassungen zu erkennen, eine frühere, von Mozart ausgewischte, mit den Bassnoten d-A d-A im System der linken Hand, und eine spätere endgültige in dunklerer Tinte, bei der Mozart im gleichen Schreibvorgang die Akkorde im oberen System und die ungewöhnlich tiefen Bassnoten im unteren System eintrug, wohl um die unbestimmten Basstöne der Pauke zu unterstützen. Es ist verständlich, dass Mozart solche Pedalnoten sonst in seinen Klavierkonzerten nicht notierte, weil er ja nicht damit rechnen konnte, dass andere Pianisten diese Sonderanfertigung zur Verfügung hätten. Es gibt

---

[4] Mit der Bezeichnung „Adagio" meint Leopold Mozart natürlich den Begriff „Langsamer Satz", der als Terminus damals noch nicht geprägt war, aber wie aus dem Sinn des Satzes hervorgeht, keineswegs ein schleppendes Tempo.
[5] Brief Leopold Mozarts an seine Tochter in St. Gilgen, 4. Januar 1786.

[6] Mozart, *Die Dokumente seines Lebens*, Hrsg. Otto Erich Deutsch, Kassel 1961, Bärenreiter, S. 211–212.
[7] vgl. *Neue Mozart-Ausgabe*, Klavierkonzerte Bd. 6, Hrsg. Horst Heussner, Hans Engel, Kassel 1961, Bärenreiter, Vorwort S. XIV–XV.

aber noch eine zweite Komposition Mozarts für Orgel oder Pedalklavier, die offensichtlich mit dieser Möglichkeit rechnete, nämlich die unvollendete Fuge in g-moll, KV 401 (375e), die heute meist in einem Arrangement für ein Klavier zu vier Händen gespielt wird. Auf ähnliche Weise könnten bei Aufführungen des d-moll-Konzerts diese tiefen Bassnoten durch einen neben dem Solisten sitzenden Spieler angeschlagen werden.

Dass Mozart auch an anderen, nicht eigens notierten Stellen zusätzlich tiefe Bassnoten, die über den Umfang seines Fortepianos hinausragten, mit Hilfe des Pedalklaviers spielte, geht unter anderem aus einem Bericht des Arztes Frank hervor.[8] Auf dem modernen Flügel könnte man im d-moll-Konzert ohne Weiteres solche tiefe Bassnoten im 1. Satz, T. 230, und im 2. Satz, T. 113, hinzufügen. Mozart dürfte das Pedalklavier aber wohl auch an anderen Stellen benutzt haben, etwa im 3. Satz, T. 148ff, und Parallelstellen.

Es ist ebenfalls Friedrich Blume zu danken, als erster in seinen Vorworten zu den Eulenburg-Partituren darauf hingewiesen zu haben, dass die durchgängige Behandlung des Klaviers als Generalbassinstrument an denjenigen Stellen, wo es nicht solistisch hervortritt, keineswegs nur konventionell gemeint war. In dem bereits zitierten Brief Leopold Mozarts vom 4. Januar 1786 heißt es: „Wenn ich das andere Concert [KV 467] hinaus schike, kannst mir dieses [d-moll, KV 466] wieder herein schicken, damit [ich] die Ziffern darauf schreiben kann." Leopold Mozart hätte sich wohl kaum die Mühe gemacht, die Generalbassziffern in die Klavierstimme während der Tutti einzutragen – nur bei Bläserstellen war sie nicht vorgesehen – wenn er nicht diesen Aufführungsstil bei seinem Sohn selbst miterlebt hätte.

Trotzdem muss heute von einem durchgehenden Continuo-Spiel auf einem modernen Konzertflügel, dessen relativ dumpfer Klang sich nicht gut mit den Streichen mischt, abgeraten werden, vor allem bei den Pianostellen. Bei einigen Fortestellen hingegen wirkt ein Mitspielen der Akkorde auch heute oft noch als Klangbereicherung, etwa im 1. Satz, T. 112–114, im 3. Satz, T. 371ff und T. 383ff, T. 414 und T. 418, vor allem bei den Schlusstakten. Beim Tutti-Schluss des B-Dur-Klavierkonzertes KV 456 hat Mozart diese Art Continuo-Akkorde sogar eigens in die Klavierstimme hineingeschrieben.[9]

Es ist anzunehmen, dass die subtilen Variationen bei den Tutti-Reprisen in T. 81 und T. 141 von Mozart durch freie Auszierungen des Soloparts jeweils 8 Takte früher vorbereitet wurden. Die eingangs erwähnte Eile bei der Partiturniederschrift mag erklären, warum er sich nicht die Zeit nehmen konnte, auch im Solopart solche „Mini-Variationen" einzutragen, wie er es sonst in vielen langsamen Sätzen – allerdings oft nachträglich – zu tun pflegte. Es ist eine heikle Frage, ob man bei modernen Aufführungen solche improvisatorischen Auszierungen wie Mozart sie sicherlich spielte, anbringen sollte oder nicht. Wenn man sich für Auszierungen bei späteren Reprisen des Ritornells entscheidet, dann sollten diese so diskret und geschmackvoll sein wie Mozarts eigene in anderen Werken.

Paul Badura-Skoda

[8] *Mozart, Die Dokumente seines Lebens*, a. a. O., S. 476.

[9] Vgl. Paul Badura-Skoda, „Über das Generalbass-Spiel in Mozarts Klavierkonzerten", *Mozart-Jahrbuch*, 1957.

PIANO CONCERTO No. 20

Wolfgang Amadeus Mozart
(1756–1791)
K466

I

Edited by Paul Badura-Skoda
© 2011 Ernst Eulenburg Ltd, London
and Ernst Eulenburg & Co GmbH, Mainz

2

4

5

8

14

18

22

52

54

55

II

Romance

74

III

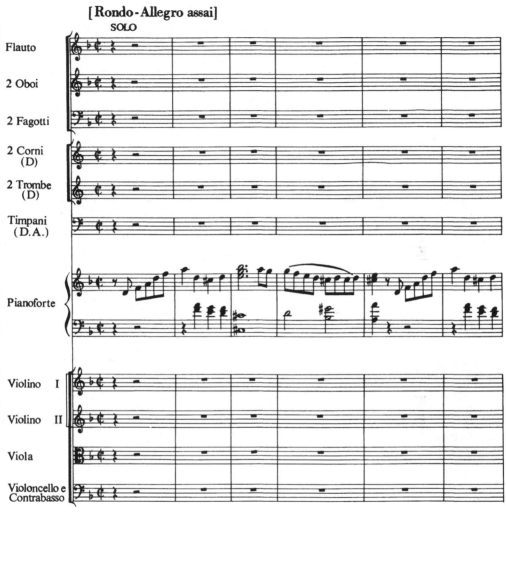

82

*) The fermata sign here probably means that a 'lead-in' was intended by Mozart.
Das Fermatenzeichen bedeutet hier dass wahrscheinlich ein Eingang gespielt werden sollte.

Two Cadenzas by Ludwig van Beethoven

Cadenza to the First Movement

Più Presto

Cadenza to the Rondo